CW00922190

Multiple-Choi
Comprehension

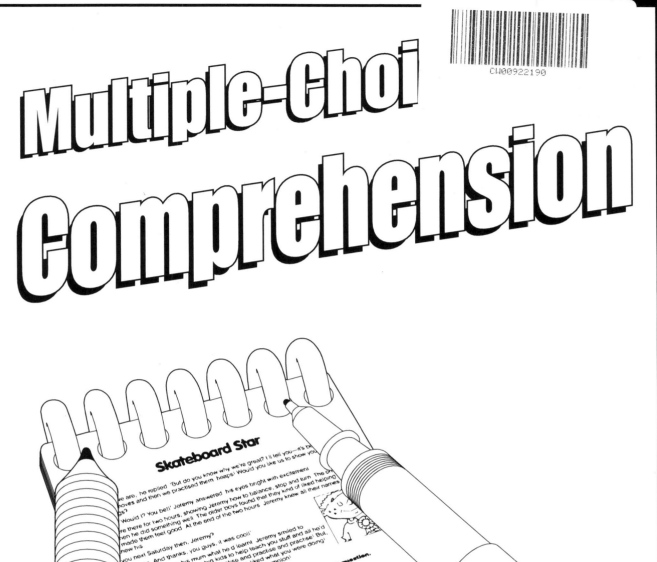

Written by Carole Booth
Published by Prim-Ed Publishing

Foreword

Multiple-Choice Comprehension is a three-book series featuring a collection of original fiction stories. The high-interest stories feature strong main characters and involving plots.

The follow-up comprehension activities are divided into two sections:

Section A –   multiple-choice questions requiring literal, interpretative and evaluative/ appreciative answers.

Section B –   varied activities designed to encourage pupils to reflect on the text, including true/false, word study, dictionary usage and sequencing.

Multiple-Choice Comprehension is a comprehensive comprehension series which also includes teachers notes, answers and English national curriculum links.

The three books in this series are:

Multiple Choice Comprehension – Lower   *(Key Stage One)*
Multiple-Choice Comprehension – Middle *(Key Stage Two – Years 3 and 4)*
Multiple-Choice Comprehension – Upper *(Key Stage Two – Years 5 and 6)*

Contents

Teachers Notes

M... ...*nsion* – Middle consists of ten original fiction stories for middle
pri... ...its corresponding activities take up three to four pages and
co...

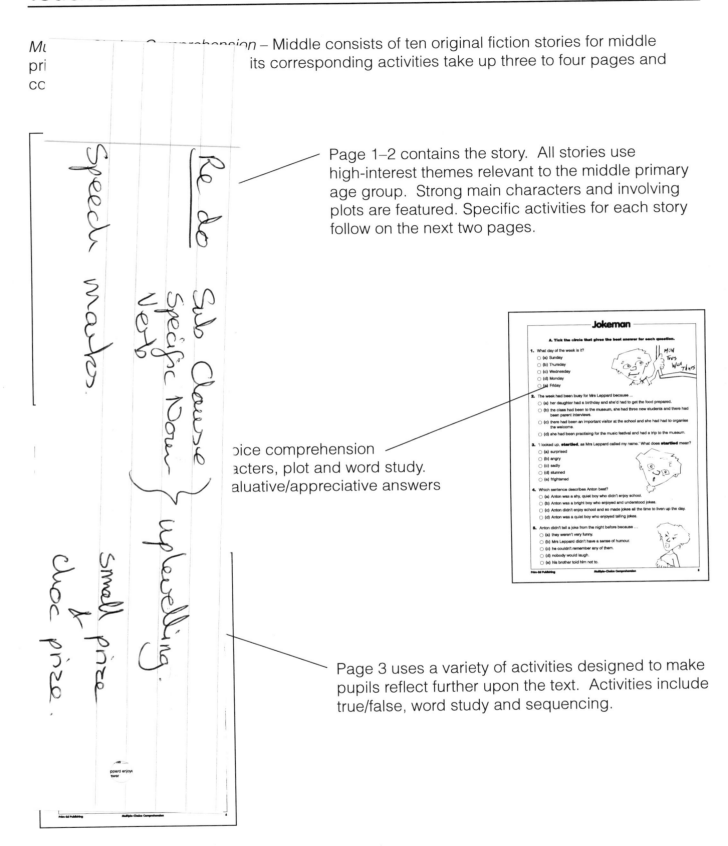

Page 1–2 contains the story. All stories use
high-interest themes relevant to the middle primary
age group. Strong main characters and involving
plots are featured. Specific activities for each story
follow on the next two pages.

...oice comprehension
...acters, plot and word study.
...aluative/appreciative answers

Page 3 uses a variety of activities designed to make
pupils reflect further upon the text. Activities include
true/false, word study and sequencing.

Further Ideas

Story themes could be used as a springboard for creative writing

Group discussion of multiple-choice alternatives

Character studies

Multiple-Choice Comprehension Curriculum Links

The activities within the three-book series Multiple-Choice Comprehension have been written to encourage pupils to demonstrate the following objectives of the English National Curriculum. The Reading and Writing Programme of Study require that pupils should be taught to:

Book	Key Stage	Programme of Study		
Lower	One	Reading	1.f	read on sight high-frequency words and other familiar words
			1.h	recognise specific parts of words, including inflectional endings
			1.l	focus on meaning derived from the text as a whole
			1.n	draw on their background knowledge and understanding of the content
			3.a	identify and describe characters, events and settings in fiction
			3.b	use their knowledge of sequence
			3.c	express preferences, giving reasons
			3.f	respond imaginatively in different ways to what they read
			6.a	read stories with familiar settings
		Writing	1.b	sequence events
			1.c	put their ideas into sentences
			3.c	use capital letters, full stops and question marks
			4.f	spell words with inflectional endings
			7.b	understand the nature of verbs
Middle	Two	Reading	2.a	use inference and deduction
			2.b	look for meaning beyond the literal
			2.c	make connections between different parts of a text
			3.a	scan texts to find information
			3.c	obtain specific information through detailed reading
			3.f	distinguish between fact and opinion
			4.g	express preferences and support their views with reference to texts
			4.h	respond imaginatively, drawing on the whole text
		Writing	3	use punctuation marks correctly in their writing
			7.a	understand word classes and grammatical functions of words, including nouns and adjectives
			9.a	imagine and explore feelings and ideas in writing
			9.d	review and comment on what has been read

Multiple-Choice Comprehension Curriculum Links

Upper	Two	Reading	2.a	use inference and deduction
			2.b	look for meanings beyond the literal
			2.c	make connections between different parts of the text
			3.a	scan texts to find information
			3.c	obtain specific information through detailed reading
			3.f	distinguish between fact and opinion
			4.g	express preferences and support their views with reference to texts
			4.h	respond imaginatively, drawing on the whole text
		Writing	3	use punctuation marks correctly in their writing
			7.a	understand word classes and grammatical functions of words, including nouns, verbs and adjectives
			9.a	imagine and explore feelings and ideas in writing
			9.d	review and comment on what has been read

A Lesson in History

'Twice history has repeated itself, and now,' thought Shona, 'it looks all set to do it again'.

The first time it happened was one bright summer's day in August, seven years ago. She could remember it like it was yesterday. She had been only six years old at the time and hadn't understood what all the fuss had been about.

They had been at the beach, the whole family. Shona remembered wearing her new swimsuit—black with big blue flowers. She had been playing at the edge of the river, by the river mouth, when she had stepped into a big hole. Under she went.

Luckily her Mum had been close by and had pulled her out of the water quickly. It had happened so fast that Shona hadn't really had time to be scared—and then she'd been safe in her mother's arms. However, her parents had made such a big fuss about it that, by the time they got home, she felt scared of the water. That fear had stayed with her as she grew up.

The second time happened at school. Their teacher took the class to the local pool in the summer and, while he walked along the edge shouting instructions, all the kids had to get in and swim. Shona didn't mind the pool too much because it felt safer and it was such hot weather that it was nice to get cool, but she still couldn't really swim properly. She could only swim for as long as she could hold her breath, then she had to stand up to get another big breath of air. Shona managed one length of the pool, with a lot of effort, but as she got to the middle of the pool for the second time, she ran out of breath again.

Shona shuddered as she remembered what happened.

You see, the middle of the pool was the deep part and Shona was a very small girl for her age. This time when she stopped to take a breath, she didn't have the energy to start off again—she had exhausted herself on the first lap—so she floundered, then panicked. Luckily one of the good swimmers realised she was in trouble and pulled her to the edge of the pool.

Since then she had avoided water, except for her daily bath or shower. Now, today, she was taking the risk of it all happening for a third time.

She stood in the water, trembling despite the hot sun and looking at the lady in front of her. She gave a crooked smile and said, 'Okay, I'm as ready as I'll ever be'.

The lady grinned back and replied, 'Well done, Shona. Getting wet is the first step towards learning to swim. Let's take it from there. I'll be right beside you all the way'.

Shona looked at the other people in the learners' swimming group. Some were about her age and some were more like her parents' age. Well, she wasn't going to leave it that long before she conquered her fear of the water and learnt to swim.

She paused for a moment in thought. 'I wonder what comes first—losing the fear of water to learn to swim, or learning to swim to help you lose your fear?' Either way, Shona decided, the only way to beat her fear was to … feel the fear and do it anyway.

A Lesson in History

A. Tick the circle that gives the best answer for each question.

1. The reason Shona gained a fear of the water in the beginning was because …
   - ○ (a) she had fallen into a hole at the edge of the river and gone under when she was six.
   - ○ (b) her parents had made a big fuss about her going under at the river.
   - ○ (c) she had never liked taking a bath.
   - ○ (d) her dad had squirted her with the hose.
   - ○ (e) she only swam at the pool.

2. What did Shona do about her problem?
   - ○ (a) She didn't swim at all.
   - ○ (b) She went to swimming classes to learn to swim.
   - ○ (c) She only went swimming with other people.
   - ○ (d) She went for walks at the beach and the river a lot.

3. Choose the word that explains what **avoided** means in this sentence 'Since then she had **avoided** the water except for her daily bath or shower'.
   - ○ (a) enjoyed
   - ○ (b) kept away from
   - ○ (c) sorted out
   - ○ (d) feared
   - ○ (e) disliked

4. Shona didn't mind going to the pool because …
   - ○ (a) she was with her class.
   - ○ (b) she felt safer.
   - ○ (c) she liked getting cool.
   - ○ (d) both (a) and (b).
   - ○ (e) both (b) and (c).

5. Shona was 'trembling' in the pool because …
   - ○ (a) the sun had gone behind the clouds.
   - ○ (b) she was frightened.
   - ○ (c) it was a cold day.
   - ○ (d) the pool water was very cold.
   - ○ (e) she was excited.

A Lesson in History

B. Complete each question as required.

1. Write the sentence that tells you Shona was nervous about the swimming class.

_____

2. Based on Shona's actions in the story, write three words which describe her character.

(a) _____ (b) _____ (c) _____

3. Write what you think the conversation would have been like between Shona and her parents just after she was pulled out of the water at the river.

_____

_____

_____

_____

_____

_____

4. What are the three main parts of the story?

(a) _____

_____

(b) _____

_____

(c) _____

_____

5. Do you feel confident in water? Rate your feelings.

Lack confidence   **Comfortable**   **Very confident**

Why do you feel this way? _____

_____

Jokeman

I am nine years old. That might not sound like much, but I'm a pretty smart kid. This morning I could tell by looking at my teacher's face that she was feeling pretty worn-out. It had been a busy week for her, with a trip to the museum, parent–teacher interviews and three new pupils in the class.

Poor Mrs Leppard, I bet she was looking forward to the weekend even more than I was.

Today she wasn't smiling at all. I know she has a good sense of humour, because she often makes jokes and puns while keeping her face looking serious. Because she looks serious, most of the other kids usually don't realise that she's made a joke. But I know. I have to stop myself from laughing loudly at times by pretending I'm coughing.

It's cool to have a teacher with a good sense of humour. Most teachers seem too serious. Maybe they've forgotten how to enjoy teaching kids. All it takes is to be able to see the fun in us and let it make them happy too. It's really easy.

Well, I don't like to see anyone unhappy or sad, because it makes me unhappy and sad too. I wondered what I could do to cheer my teacher up a bit. Then I remembered, today is Wednesday—it is joke day! Just the thing!

'Anton.'

I looked up, startled, as Mrs Leppard called my name.

'Yes, Mrs Leppard?' I answered, wondering what she wanted me for. Then I realised, of course, she was calling the class register. Joke time comes next. What joke could I tell that was really funny? Funny enough to make my teacher laugh?

Time was running out. I tried hard to remember the ones my mum and brother had told me last night, but I couldn't remember any of them.

Oh no, the register had finished and they'd started telling jokes. Matthew had just finished telling his and some of the class giggled a bit, but I was too worried to even notice.

Then I had an idea. I put my hand up.

'Yes, Anton? Do you have a joke for us?' Mrs Leppard asked.

I stood up.

'Well, not really,' I replied, 'but I was going to bring my brother along to class today—he's a bit of a joke!'.

It worked! A big grin spread across her face and she chuckled with delight.

At last my teacher was happy.

Jokeman strikes again!

Jokeman

A. Tick the circle that gives the best answer for each question.

1. What day of the week is it?
- ○ (a) Sunday
- ○ (b) Thursday
- ○ (c) Wednesday
- ○ (d) Monday
- ○ (e) Friday

2. The week had been busy for Mrs Leppard because ...
- ○ (a) her daughter had a birthday and she'd had to get the food prepared.
- ○ (b) the class had been to the museum, she had three new pupils and there had been parent interviews.
- ○ (c) there had been an important visitor at the school and she had had to organise the welcome.
- ○ (d) she had been practising for the music festival and had a trip to the museum.

3. 'I looked up, **startled**, as Mrs Leppard called my name.' What does **startled** mean?
- ○ (a) surprised
- ○ (b) angry
- ○ (c) sadly
- ○ (d) stunned
- ○ (e) frightened

4. Which sentence describes Anton best?
- ○ (a) Anton was a shy, quiet boy who didn't enjoy school.
- ○ (b) Anton was a bright boy who enjoyed and understood jokes.
- ○ (c) Anton didn't enjoy school and so made jokes all the time to liven up the day.
- ○ (d) Anton was a quiet boy who enjoyed telling jokes.

5. Anton didn't tell a joke from the night before because ...
- ○ (a) they weren't very funny.
- ○ (b) Mrs Leppard didn't have a sense of humour.
- ○ (c) he couldn't remember any of them.
- ○ (d) nobody would laugh.
- ○ (e) his brother told him not to.

Jokeman

B. Complete each question as required.

1. True or false?

(a) At first Mrs Leppard was bright and smiling. ☐ True ☐ False

(b) Mrs Leppard kept her face serious when she told jokes. ☐ True ☐ False

(c) Anton told a joke his mum had told him the night before. ☐ True ☐ False

(d) Joke time was at the end of the day. ☐ True ☐ False

(e) Anton's joke worked. ☐ True ☐ False

(f) Mrs Leppard doesn't like jokes in her class. ☐ True ☐ False

2. An antonym is a word which has the opposite meaning to a given word. For example, **hot** is the antonym of **cold.**

Give antonyms for these words from the story.

new	
smiling	
happy	
last	
answered	
finished	

3. Complete these sentences.

(a) On this day, Mrs Leppard looked _____.

(b) Anton liked having a teacher with a good sense of _____.

(c) Matthew's joke was quite funny and the class _____ a bit.

(d) Anton told a joke about his _____.

4. Do you think that Mrs Leppard enjoyed having Anton in her class? Give reasons for your answer.

_____

_____

_____

Skateboard Star

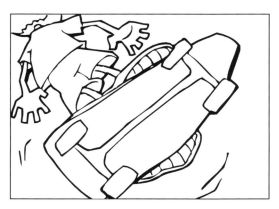

The sun was shining and a gentle breeze was blowing. It was a nice day to be outside.

The silence was broken by shouts and yells. Looking through the bushes you could see who was making all the noise—eight boys aged between 10 and 12, racing around on skateboards at the skateboard area. They skimmed over the humps and hills, trying to jump the wooden ramps that were placed around. You could tell they were having some kind of contest. They were all trying to do better than each other.

One after the other they would glide around the course, leaping about, with their skateboards looking like they were glued to their shoes. Twisting and turning, they would jump high into the air in a display of total control of their boards—well, maybe not quite total control. The shouts and yells were loudest when someone came off and landed on the concrete. A bit of blood seemed to make it even more fun for them. It was easy to tell that these boys had been practising for years—they were good; in fact, they were very good.

There was a ninth boy, about seven years old, standing near, just watching them, his skateboard in his hand.

The older boys finally finished their fun. They were tired and hot.

'Come on, kid,' one called. 'It's all yours now. Show us what you can do.'

The boy shook his head and looked down at his shoes.

'There's no way I'm going to try anything in front of them,' he thought. 'They're too good. I can't really do anything yet, so they'd probably have a good laugh at me.'

'Please yourself, kid,' the older boy said. 'Come on guys, let's go up the street and grab a drink.'

As he watched them go, the small boy put his board on the ground and started to skate with it. He hadn't had it long. His nanna had given it to him for his birthday six months ago, in the middle of winter. He hadn't used it much then, but now it was summer and he wanted to learn how to use it.

Jeremy (that was his name) lived close to the park, so he had decided that he was going to come often to practise. He'd seen these boys before when he'd come to practise, but he'd watched them through the bushes for a while and then gone home again. Today he'd decided that it was his park too, so he'd just wait for them to go away and then he'd have a go.

It was cool fun just kneeling on the board and going down the little hills—he could do that for ages. He was having so much fun that he didn't hear the older boys come back until someone started to laugh.

He looked up and his face turned red. Oh no! They'd been watching him.

Before he could run away, the boy who'd spoken to him before said, 'Hey, kid. It's OK. Don't let Dion here bother you. He's just an idiot. How long have you had your board? It looks quite new'.

'I got it for my birthday, six months ago. I'm just learning, not like you guys—you're great!'

Skateboard Star

'Well, sure we are,' he replied. 'But do you know why we're great? I'll tell you—it's because we learnt the moves and then we practised them, heaps! Would you like us to show you how to do some things?'

'Oh, boy! Would I? You bet!' Jeremy answered, his eyes bright with excitement.

They were there for two hours, showing Jeremy how to balance, stop and turn. The only shouts were when he did something well. The older boys found that they kind of liked helping a little kid—it made them feel good. At the end of the two hours, Jeremy knew all their names and they knew his.

'See you next Saturday then, Jeremy?'

'You bet, Sam. And thanks, you guys, it was cool!'

Running home to show his mum what he'd learnt, Jeremy smiled to himself. It was so cool to have big kids to help teach you stuff and all he'd have to do to be like them was to practise and practise and practise! But, hey. No big deal. Practice was fun when you liked what you were doing! Who knows, one day he could be a skateboard champion!

A. Tick the circle that gives the best answer for each question.

1. Jeremy had …

○ (a) owned his skateboard for six months.

○ (b) owned his skateboard for several years.

○ (c) just got his skateboard.

○ (d) borrowed the skateboard from a friend.

2. After the boys had left …

○ (a) Jeremy went home.

○ (b) Jeremy tried going over the jumps.

○ (c) another group of older boys arrived.

○ (d) Jeremy tried kneeling on the board and going down little hills.

3. At first Jeremy didn't want to show the older boys what he could do because …

○ (a) he was scared he'd fall off.

○ (b) he thought they would laugh at him.

○ (c) he was embarrassed that he would be better than they were.

○ (d) he thought they'd tell the kids at school.

4. Sam was …

○ (a) older, unkind, skilful and generous.

○ (b) Jeremy's age, understanding and kind.

○ (c) younger, thoughtful, a good skateboarder and helpful.

○ (d) older, caring, skilful and helpful.

Skateboard Star

1. Number these events as they happened in the story.

☐ (a) Jeremy went home to show his mum what he had learnt.

☐ (b) The older boys were having a competition.

☐ (c) The older boys helped Jeremy.

☐ (d) Jeremy tried kneeling on his skateboard and going down little hills.

☐ (e) The older boys came back from the shop.

2. Write another way the story could have ended. Start from: 'He looked up and his face turned red. Oh no! They'd been watching him.'

_____

_____

_____

_____

_____

_____

3. If you practise a skill often _____

_____

4. Comment on the actions of the older boys towards Jeremy.

_____

_____

5. (a) Is it good to share knowledge and skills with others? _____

(b) What skills could you teach others? _____

_____

(c) Write how you would explain/teach one of these skills to someone.

_____

_____

_____

Melissa's Story

Hi, my name is Matthew. I am nine years old. I live in an old house that Dad and Mum are doing up. Dad is always busy working on the house. He says he should get it nearly finished this year. It's in a bit of a mess at the moment. Mum says that it's because it's hard to keep things clean and tidy when Dad keeps knocking out walls, sawing up wood and making the place look like a war zone.

There are four people in our family—there's Dad, Mum, Steven—my little brother—and me. There used to be five people in our family. I used to have an older sister, but now I'm the oldest child.

My sister's name was Melissa. I miss her heaps. I'd like to tell you about her, because she was special. This is Melissa's story.

Melissa was 10 years old. She was pretty, with long brown hair that came down past her waist. Her eyes were blue and she was quite tall for her age. She liked all the normal sort of stuff girls seem to like; you know, dolls, Girl Guides and that sort of thing. But she also liked other things, like animals. She was very interested in orcas (that's the proper name for 'killer whales'). She did a really neat project on them. It took her ages and she looked in heaps of books to find out things about them. Mum was pleased, because she got 95% for it. She saw *Free Willy* (that film about the boy and the orca) three times and cried every time.

Melissa liked all living creatures. She could never understand why people kill animals or treat them badly. It upset her a lot when she found out about tigers being killed for old Chinese medicines and elephants and rhinos being killed for their ivory. Then there are whales and dolphins being killed every day, rare birds' eggs stolen by collectors and even shellfish being killed for their shells, so that people can have something pretty to look at in their china cabinets.

I think I know why people do these sorts of things—I think that it's either that they are greedy for money, or they just don't care about the world like Melissa did. I sometimes wonder if Melissa was too good to be here and that's why she died. It is scary to think that a kid can die, but it can happen. I don't quite know how it happened to Melissa. Mum said it was 'medical misadventure'—whatever that means. I just know that she was very sick and had to have an operation.

She came home for a while afterwards and looked good, but then something happened and she died quite suddenly and unexpectedly. Dad said something went very wrong and the hospital is checking to find out what. It is taking a long time. Mum and Dad are still very sad about losing Melissa.

Mum talks about Melissa a lot. Dad doesn't. He just works hard at his job and at fixing the house up. I think he gets so tired that he doesn't have time to think about Melissa, he just falls asleep really fast. I think that is easier for him than having time to think about her.

It seems strange to me that I'm the oldest kid in my family now. It seems strange too, that I can walk past her bedroom and not tease her about boys and stuff. We all really miss her a lot. There is not much we can do to stop the hurting, but at least we can remember all the good times we had together. Like when she wanted an orca for her birthday, but instead Mum bought her goldfish. She was so thrilled to have them you'd have thought they really were orcas!

Yes, it does seem strange not having her around any more, but you know something? She will always be with us—in our hearts.

Melissa's Story

A. Tick the circle that gives the best answer for each question.

1. How many people were there in Matthew's family before Melissa died?

○ (a) three

○ (b) four

○ (c) six

○ (d) five

2. Melissa was …

○ (a) tall, with long black hair and blue eyes.

○ (b) quite tall, with long brown hair and blue eyes.

○ (c) short, with long brown hair and brown eyes.

○ (d) quite tall, with short brown hair and blue eyes.

3. Melissa was very interested in …

○ (a) learning about and protecting all animals.

○ (b) killer whales only.

○ (c) whales and dolphins.

○ (d) elephants and tigers.

○ (e) Girl Guides.

4. Dad missed Melissa a lot but worked all the time …

○ (a) so he could get the house finished quickly.

○ (b) so he didn't have time to think about her too much.

○ (c) to help the rest of the family.

○ (d) because the family needed the money.

○ (e) because he enjoyed it.

5. Melissa will always be with the family because …

○ (a) they have a photo of her.

○ (b) of her goldfish.

○ (c) of the love in their hearts.

○ (d) her bedroom is still there.

○ (e) Mum talks about her.

Melissa's Story

1. (a) What is the author's name?

_____

(b) What relation is the author to Melissa?

_____

2. True or false?

(a) Melissa had to have an operation because she was very sick. ☐ True ☐ False

(b) Mum and Dad didn't expect Melissa to live. ☐ True ☐ False

(c) Melissa didn't enjoy doing school work. ☐ True ☐ False

(d) Matthew felt strange about being the oldest child in the family. ☐ True ☐ False

(e) Melissa was disappointed about the goldfish. ☐ True ☐ False

3. What do you think Matthew meant when he said, 'I sometimes wonder if Melissa was too good to be here?'.

_____

_____

4. Complete the grid with the words used in the story.

adjectives	nouns
	eggs
	creatures
china	
oldest	
	medicines

5. Melissa cared about animals. She didn't like people killing or treating them badly. How do you feel about this? What do you think about animals being killed for medicines or ivory or food? Do you think the reason why animals are killed makes a difference?

_____

_____

_____

_____

Best Friends

There are five of us—Chris, Daniel, Adam, Leigh and me, Brad. We're all best friends. We've been best friends since nursery. We hang about together at school and play at each other's homes after school. We aren't in the same classes at school, but it doesn't matter.

We have had a lot of fun together, even though we always seem to get into trouble. It isn't that we're bad on purpose or look for trouble; it seems trouble finds us.

Like the time we thought we'd kick a football around a bit after school one day. Well, what's wrong with that, you might think. I'll tell you what happened.

The five of us were there for 20 minutes, having a bit of fun, when Fabian, Sam and a few others came along. So we got into teams and started playing a good game on the back field. What we didn't know was that our parents were getting worried, because we hadn't told anyone where we were.

My mum wanted to go to town, so she rang up Adam's mum, because she thought I was over there, but Adam's mum thought we were at Chris's, so she rang his mum. We weren't there, so she thought we must all be at Leigh's. She rang my mum back. Things got a bit tricky after my mum rang Leigh's mum and we weren't there either. They started to imagine all sorts of terrible things that could have happened to us—you know how mothers can imagine the worst. I guess they really started to panic after the school told Mum we weren't there. You see, the back field is hidden from the school office, so they couldn't see us.

Boy, were we in deep trouble when we got home! We have to let our parents know where we are now, which I suppose isn't a bad thing if it stops them from getting mad with us.

Another time we went to the BMX track for some fun and we ended up having a war, throwing hunks of dirt at some other kids who thought they owned the place. Chris had a big bruise on his cheek where he got hit by a missile. His mum was pretty upset—so was mine when she saw how dirty my clothes were.

However, some bigger trouble happened at Easter which makes me wonder whether I should call them my best friends any more. It just doesn't seem right that kids I call my friends should steal. Of course, they didn't say they stole those Easter eggs from the shop. They said they 'pinched' or 'nicked' them—but it's the same thing, isn't it?

My Dad owns a shop. He sells bicycles and stuff. He told me that every little thing that people 'shoplift', he's had to pay for in the first place. That means he doesn't get that money back, so it's just like someone stealing money from his wallet. Dad works hard at his job. He has to pay rent for the building, advertising, electricity and things, as well as the people he buys the bicycles from. He's still paying off the loan he got from the bank to buy the business with. The last thing he needs is people stealing his stuff and I'm sure it's the same with the owner of any shop.

I know my friends think it's a joke—pinching stuff. They think they'll never get caught. They tried to get me to do it, too. Do you think best friends should try to make you do things you don't think you should? I really would have liked an Easter egg, but it didn't feel right and even though they teased me and called me a chicken, I didn't do it. Do you think I was a 'chicken'?

What do you think I should do about my 'best friends'? Please tell me.

Best Friends

A. Tick the circle that gives the best answer for each question.

1. The boys had been friends …

   ○ (a) since they started school together.

   ○ (b) since nursery.

   ○ (c) since they were in the same class at school.

   ○ (d) since their mums had become friendly.

   ○ (e) since they were four years of age.

2. The boys got into trouble over the football game because …

   ○ (a) they weren't allowed to play football on the school grounds after school.

   ○ (b) their mums didn't know where they were.

   ○ (c) they broke a window during the game.

   ○ (d) they had taken someone's ball.

   ○ (e) they were late home.

3. Brad's mum was upset about the dirt fight because …

   ○ (a) Chris got hurt.

   ○ (b) she didn't like fighting.

   ○ (c) his clothes got dirty.

   ○ (d) she didn't know where he was.

   ○ (e) Brad got hurt.

4. Brad's 'friends' stole …

   ○ (a) money from his Dad's wallet.

   ○ (b) a bicycle from his Dad's shop.

   ○ (c) a football.

   ○ (d) Easter eggs from a shop.

   ○ (e) someone's BMX bike.

5. Brad didn't know whether he should call the boys his best friends anymore. Why?

   ○ (a) Because they stole from the shop.

   ○ (b) Because they were always getting him into trouble.

   ○ (c) Because they tried to make him do something he didn't want to do.

   ○ (d) Both (a) and (b).

   ○ (e) Both (a) and (c).

Best Friends

B. Complete each question as required.

1. Put the telephone conversations in order.

- ☐ (a) Brad's mum rang the school.
- ☐ (b) Adam's mum rang Chris's mum.
- ☐ (c) Brad's mum rang Adam's mum.
- ☐ (d) Adam's mum rang Brad's mum.
- ☐ (e) Brad's mum rang Leigh's mum.

2. This story is called 'Best Friends'. Can you think of another title?

_____

_____

_____

3. What do you think Brad should do about his best friends?

_____

_____

_____

_____

4. **Steal, shoplift, pinch** and **nick** all mean the same thing. They are called synonyms. Give a synonym for each of these words from the story.

(a) dirty – _____

(b) big – _____

(c) worried – _____

(d) right – _____

5. Explain in your own words the meaning of these words from the story.

(a) panic – _____

(b) missile – _____

(c) loan – _____

(d) imagine – _____

6. Make a list of the people Brad's dad pays. Alongside each, write what he pays them for.

pays money to ...	pays money for ...

The Secret Wish

Dane thought his mum was a bit square. He had always secretly wished she could be more like Corey's mum. Corey's mum liked to have fun. She often wore the most outrageous clothes—bright reds, purples, pinks and yellows, and even a baseball cap and jogging shoes.

Corey's mum liked to go for rides on her 10-speed mountain bike and enjoyed going down to the arcade to play 'spacies' with Corey for an hour or more. It was a real pity that Dane's mum wasn't more like her. Well, that's what he thought until the day he decided that his mum should learn to use their computer.

'Come on, Mum. Have a go on it,' Dane said, urging his mum to try the computer out. They'd had it a year and the only time his mother got anywhere near it was to dust it. His dad used it quite a bit for working out money and things, but his mum was just plain scared of it.

'You know I'm no good at these sorts of things, Dane. I can't even set the video properly,' his mother replied anxiously.

'But I'll help you, Mum. I know all about it.'

That was perhaps a little bit of a lie, but he did know a lot.

'It's really easy. All you have to do to start it up is push this button here—you can do that, Mum. Then you move the mouse …'

'Eeeek!' screamed his mother, climbing on to the chair. 'What mouse?'

'Mum! That's what this thing is called—it's a mouse.'

Dane was trying hard to be patient with his mother, but he thought, 'How silly can you get!'.

His mother's face was a bit red as she climbed down from the chair. She was so embarrassed that she decided to try very hard to listen to what Dane wanted to teach her. She didn't want her son to think she was a total idiot.

Dane showed her how to load a program. He got her to load the writing program, but then neither of them could think of anything to write, so he loaded one of his favourite games, 'Gauntlet'.

'Here you are, Mum,' he said, handing her a joystick and grabbing the other one himself. 'You're the yellow guy, Merlin the Wizard. He throws yellow potion bottles to kill the bad guys. I'm Questor the Elf. That's the green guy. I shoot the bad guys with my arrows. The idea of the game is to knock down as many bad guys as we can and try to find the keys to open the door to a different passage.'

His mother was already firing the joystick.

'Look, Dane! I got one! And there's another one down. Come on you losers, see if you can get me! I think I've got the hang of it now, Dane. It's quite fun really, isn't it?'

Dane looked quickly over at his mum. Boy, she was really getting the hang of it all right and she was getting quite 'carried away'—that was what she called it when Dane got so excited that he yelled and made strange noises. Could this really be his mother? He was pleased—maybe she wasn't quite so square after all.

A month later and Dane still hadn't been able to play on the computer after school or even on the weekends, because his mum or dad were always using it. And the worst thing was that Dane knew he only had himself to blame!

Three months later, Dane's mother finally got tired of playing video games and let Dane have more time on the computer. However, she was now starting to write stories for kids on it, so he still had to share it with her.

She thanked Dane for teaching her how to use the computer. She said that she hadn't known she could do it until she tried. It's like that for us too, isn't it? We never know what we can do if we never try.

The Secret Wish

A. Tick the circle that gives the best answer for each question.

1. Dane's mum hadn't used the computer because ...

   ○ (a) Dane and his father were always using it.

   ○ (b) she worked full-time and just didn't have time.

   ○ (c) she was scared of it.

   ○ (d) she didn't have any need to use it.

   ○ (e) she didn't like computer games.

2. Which do you think is correct?

   ○ (a) Dane's mum said she enjoyed the game so she didn't hurt his feelings.

   ○ (b) Dane's mum quite enjoyed the game.

   ○ (c) Dane's mum was really surprised at how much she enjoyed the game.

   ○ (d) Dane's mum played the game but didn't enjoy it at all.

3. After a while, Dane's mother ...

   ○ (a) learnt how to use other programs.

   ○ (b) stopped using the computer.

   ○ (c) kept playing Dane's computer games.

   ○ (d) helped her husband with the accounts.

   ○ (e) wouldn't let Dane use the computer.

4. Dane thought his mum was a bit square. What does 'a bit square' mean?

   ○ (a) She was short and a bit fat.

   ○ (b) She was a bit old-fashioned.

   ○ (c) She was a bit of a rebel.

   ○ (d) She was honest.

   ○ (e) She was outrageous.

5. Dane first thought his mum wasn't quite so square when ...

   ○ (a) she loaded a computer program.

   ○ (b) she got 'carried away' playing the computer game.

   ○ (c) she jumped on the chair to avoid the 'mouse'.

   ○ (d) she started to write stories for kids on the computer.

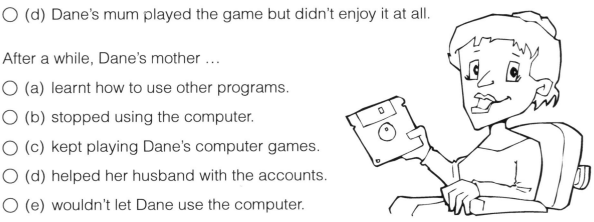

The Secret Wish

1. What three things did Dane like about Corey's mum?

(a) _____

(b) _____

(c) _____

2. True or false?

(a) Dane's mother was confident using technology. ☐ True ☐ False

(b) Dane's mother took a long time to learn how to play the game. ☐ True ☐ False

(c) Dane's mother knew what a computer mouse was. ☐ True ☐ False

(d) At first Dane regretted teaching his mum about the computer. ☐ True ☐ False

(e) Dane's mother eventually got tired of playing video games. ☐ True ☐ False

3. Decide on the three main events in the story and list them in order.

(a) _____

_____

(b) _____

_____

(c) _____

_____

4. Find the meaning of these words from the story.

(a) outrageous – _____

(b) anxiously – _____

(c) arcade – _____

(d) total – _____

5. What three things do you really like about your mum?

(a) _____

(b) _____

(c) _____

Kid Sister

Cody was nine years old. He had dark curly hair, brown eyes, and a cheeky grin. Cody had lots of friends. In fact life was pretty good … except for one thing. Cody had a problem. It was called Suzie. Suzie was small, with long curly hair and brown eyes like Cody's. She was only five years old. She was Cody's little sister!

Now it wasn't that he minded having a little sister, the problem was that everything he wanted to do, she wanted to do too! And everywhere he wanted to go, she wanted to go too! He hated it. Like last week, when he wanted to go down to the shop to buy a new baseball card.

'Mum, can I run down to the shop? I want to buy the new baseball card that's just come out.'

'Me too, Mum. Can I go, too?' said a loud voice from the sofa.

Darn, he'd been hoping she was too busy watching TV to hear what he was saying to Mum. No such luck. 'And Mum always takes her side,' he thought.

'Yes Cody, you can go, and take Suzie with you. She has pocket money that she wants to spend.'

'Aww, Mum, do I have to take her? She dawdles and she takes ages to make up her mind when she's buying sweets,' Cody moaned to his mother.

'Yes, you do,' said his mum firmly, 'if you want to go too'.

Then there was the time he'd wanted to go to the movies with his mates. His friend's mother was taking them to the cinema and picking them up afterwards. It would be cool to get away from his family (especially his little sister!) and have a good time with his friends. Just the four of them.

And then, you guessed it, his little sister found out about their plans and she wanted to go, too! When his mother rang up Paul's mum to see if she would mind taking an extra kid, poor Cody had never felt so embarrassed (except maybe the time when his shorts got pulled down in a rugby game). Paul's mum didn't mind, even if Paul did! Cody was furious, and his friends were furious with him!

Cody wondered if all little sisters were such a problem to other kids, or did he have the only one in the world like this. It seemed to Cody that there was nothing he could do without his sister hanging around. Even at school she managed to find him at playtime and lunchtime, no matter how hard he tried to hide from her. Why did she do it? Was it just to embarrass him in front of his friends?

Finally, Cody couldn't stand it any longer. He had to tell his mum how he felt.

'Well, Cody,' his mother said, 'I'm afraid you'll have to put up with it a little longer. Don't forget, Suzie's only been at school a few weeks, and she hasn't made any friends of her own yet. Besides she thinks her big brother is pretty neat fun'.

'You mean I have to take her *everywhere*?' Cody moaned.

'Just for a while,' Mum promised. 'Once she makes new friends, believe me, she won't want to hang around *you* any more.'

Cody wasn't sure he liked the way Mum said that!

Kid Sister

A. Tick the circle that gives the best answer for each question.

1. Cody's little sister, Suzie, had …

○ (a) short curly hair and brown eyes.

○ (b) short curly hair and blue eyes.

○ (c) straight hair and brown eyes.

○ (d) long curly hair and blue eyes.

○ (e) long curly hair and brown eyes.

2. Cody didn't want to take Suzie to the shop because …

○ (a) she walked slowly.

○ (b) he was embarrassed someone might see her.

○ (c) she took ages to spend her money.

○ (d) all of the above.

○ (e) both (a) and (c).

3. What made Cody's friends furious?

○ (a) The cinema shop had run out of popcorn.

○ (b) Cody took Suzie to the movies too.

○ (c) The movie was babyish.

○ (d) Suzie laughed during the movie.

○ (e) His mother came to the movies with them.

4. Suzie wanted to go to the shop …

○ (a) to buy an ice-cream.

○ (b) to spend some pocket money.

○ (c) to buy a baseball card.

○ (d) to annoy Cody.

5. Cody realised Suzie hung around him because …

○ (a) she wanted to annoy him.

○ (b) his mother told her to.

○ (c) she didn't have friends of her own.

○ (d) she liked her big brother.

○ (e) (c) and (d).

Kid Sister

1. Which setting—the shop, the movies or school—do you think would have been most embarrassing for Cody?

_____

Give reasons for your answer. _____

_____

_____

2. Colour the best answer.

(a) Mum spoiled Suzie.

yes	no	perhaps

(b) Cody wondered if all little sisters were like Suzie.

yes	no	perhaps

(c) Cody and Suzie had similar features.

yes	no	perhaps

(d) Going to the movies with Suzie was the most embarrassing thing that had happened to Cody.

yes	no	perhaps

3. 'Me too, Mum. Can I go, too?' said a loud voice from the sofa.
Look carefully at the speaking punctuation. Use it to help you write a likely conversation between Suzie and Cody on the way to the shop.

_____

_____

_____

_____

_____

4. Choose your sister or brother or a friend's sister or brother. Describe what they look like, their personality and what you like about them.

_____

_____

_____

_____

_____

No Party for Blake

Blake had never felt so lonely. Here it was, three weeks away from his ninth birthday, and no-one to invite to it. Mum said he could have a party—but who could he invite? He'd only been at the school for a week and he didn't know anyone well enough to call them a friend, and no-one seemed to want him to join in … and Blake was too shy to ask.

He missed his old school, and his old house. But most of all Blake missed his dad. There was just him and his mum now. His parents had separated. His dad had got a new job in another town so they had moved to be close to his mum's family. At first he thought it was all his fault. He'd wished he hadn't been so noisy or naughty—then maybe Dad would have stayed.

Even after his mum explained the real reasons, he still felt guilty. That was when he decided to be a really quiet, good boy for Mum. Maybe then she'd tell Dad he could come back home again.

Blake didn't realise that his mum could see that he was trying so hard to be good, that he'd become too quiet and too well-mannered. He was trying to be perfect. In other words, he wasn't acting like a normal healthy boy should. She was quite worried. And that's why she had brought him along tonight to Cubs.

'He's been worse since we moved. It's not natural for a boy to be so quiet,' she was telling the man by the door of the hall. 'I know he still misses his dad.'

The man flashed a grin at Blake and said, 'Welcome to Cub Scouts, Blake. I hope you enjoy yourself. We do all sorts of fun and interesting things here. Have you ever cooked a marshmallow and chocolate biscuit sandwich before, or gone on a hike up the mountain? No? Well, you might get to do that this summer'.

Blake stared at the Cub leader in his smart uniform … a marshmallow and chocolate biscuit sandwich? Yum, that sounded good. Then he looked at all the noisy kids running around the hall. It seemed that they all knew each other, and they were all wearing a smart uniform. Some of them had a lot of badges, Blake wondered what they were for. He felt like the odd man out … again.

'Hi, I'm Mark,' said a ginger-haired boy. 'Are you going to join Cubs?'

'Oh, hello. I don't know. Mum wants me to, but I don't know,' Blake replied.

Just then the leader shouted, 'Pack, pack, pack!' and to Blake's surprise that noisy bunch of kids shouted 'Pack' back and then all lined up, quietly standing to attention like soldiers!

As he was introduced, he was able to get a good look at them and he got another surprise. Grinning back at him were two girls! 'Girls, in Cub Scouts?' he thought. It wasn't until later that Mark told him that it wasn't just for boys any more, and girls could do anything the boys could, and often did it better!

It was a noisy night and although Blake wasn't used to all the noise and activity, he enjoyed himself (which was his third surprise that night!). How could you not enjoy a relay where you picked up jellybeans with chopsticks—and then you ate them. It was a Japan night, so they did origami (paper folding). Mark said it was to earn their bronze Weiro badge—whatever that was! Blake was having trouble understanding the different badges, but it was all very interesting and sounded like fun.

No Party for Blake

The next week he had a bit of a cold, but when his mother told him he could stay in bed instead of going to school, he said, 'No way, Mum, I want to go to Cubs tonight'.

They had other games and made a neat heart necklace for a Mother's Day present. Blake carefully wrapped his in pretty paper after hanging it on a silver thread. He hid it behind his back when his mum came to pick him up, so she couldn't see it. Mother's Day was two days away. He could hardly wait to give it to her; it was truly the best thing he had ever made. He was very proud.

The next week Blake was even more proud as he stood in his Cub uniform and made his Cub promise to Akela the leader. He was now a real Cub. He had a jersey, his scarf and woggle, and his Cub badge book. He knew what to do with that! He was going to get his Mum to help him read it, to sort out what badges he could earn. He might earn his 'home help' badge first. You got to cook a meal of eggs, sausages and potatoes for that badge. That sounded like an interesting thing to try.

Blake was still thinking …'Oh, and another thing I have to do tonight before the Cubs go home. I have to give out my party invitations. Sure hope Mum didn't mind me inviting all my friends. All twelve of them'.

A. Tick the circle that gives the best answer for each question.

1. Blake's Mum and Dad divorced because …
- ○ (a) Blake was too quiet and too well-mannered.
- ○ (b) Blake was noisy and naughty.
- ○ (c) Blake's dad had got a job overseas.
- ○ (d) None of the above.

2. When Blake had a cold why didn't he want to stay home from school?
- ○ (a) They were going on a class trip.
- ○ (b) He thought his mum was just fussing.
- ○ (c) He didn't want to have to go to the doctor.
- ○ (d) It was Cubs night.

3. Which words best describe how Blake felt about the present he made for his mum?
- ○ (a) excited and expectant
- ○ (b) proud and nervous
- ○ (c) proud and excited
- ○ (d) unhappy but proud

4. Which badge was Blake thinking of working for first?
- ○ (a) origami folding
- ○ (b) bronze Weiro
- ○ (c) home help
- ○ (d) hiking

No Party for Blake

B. Complete each question as required.

1. Order the sentences as they happened in the story.

☐ (a) Blake became very quiet and good.

☐ (b) Blake moved to a new school.

☐ (c) Blake made Mum a Mother's Day present.

☐ (d) Blake gave out his birthday invitations.

☐ (e) Blake joined Cubs.

2. Finish each sentence.

(a) Blake didn't play with the groups at the school because _____

_____

(b) Blake's mum took him to cubs because _____

(c) Blake enjoyed the relay because _____

3. This story is called 'No Party for Blake.' Can you think of another title?

_____

4. List the three surprises Blake had on the first night he went to Cubs.

(a) _____

(b) _____

(c) _____

5. Find the word in the story which means the same as these words or phrases.

(a) faultless – _____   (b) group – _____

(c) what you would expect – _____

(d) feeling very pleased, satisfied – _____

6. Write about a club or group you belong to. Give details about what you do, the uniform you wear, any rules the club has and what you like about it.

_____

_____

_____

_____

Midnight Meeting

It was 15 minutes to midnight and the moon was a luminous glow in the cloudy sky. 'What on earth made me say I'd meet them in the graveyard of the old abandoned church? I must be mad, but it's too late now,' I thought, 'I'm almost there'. I could see the headstones of the graves standing in stark contrast to the dark colour of the stone church.

'Where are Steve, Nathan and Daniel? They said they'd be waiting here for me,' I whispered as I looked around. I could see shadows everywhere, nothing seemed real any more. I was scared. They had to be here. I'd brought the video camera just like they told me to. Dad would kill me if he found out.

The wind howled. We were in for a storm. The noise sent shivers up my spine. It started to pour with rain and I stuffed the camera under my jacket and ran for the doors of the old church. The hinges were rusting off and I was able to push one door open wide enough to slip in.

It was darker inside. I couldn't see anything for a minute while my eyes adjusted to the gloom. I walked further in, feeling my way along the seats. Suddenly, my hand touched something clammy, cold and wet. I choked back a scream that rose in my throat, my hand flying to my mouth. My fear was a tangible thing. Whatever it was in the seat moved. It moaned, and started to rise. This time I really did scream! And so did 'The Thing'. It leapt up with a high-pitched shriek and then collapsed with a groan.

By this time I was sure it was one of the ghosts said to haunt the old church and my mind had gone kind of crazy, like I was in some kind of nightmare world or something. My mouth was dry and my stomach was tied in knots of fear, I couldn't think straight and my instinct was to get away as fast as I could. I forgot all about my friends, the storm and even Dad's video camera (which, luckily, was still tucked securely under my parka where I'd put it earlier) in my haste to escape.

As I clambered through the laundry window back home, the hallway light went on. 'Douglas, is that you?' my dad called, coming down the hall. There was nowhere to hide. I had to own up to my midnight wanderings.

'Yes, Dad,' I said, as he approached. I must have looked a fright because he stood for a minute staring at me.

With a towel wrapped around me and a cup of hot cocoa in my hands, I had to tell my parents the whole story of how I let myself be provoked into doing something I knew I shouldn't, just because of a silly dare. I really felt ashamed now that I was safe at home, but I remembered how scared I felt out there in the graveyard and the church … the church! I had to tell Dad about the ghost I saw in the church!

Dad didn't believe that what I'd seen was a ghost, but he did believe that something had really scared me, so he set off with a big torch and his raincoat to see for himself.

It was still raining when he arrived back an hour later, carrying something large in his arms. Mum gasped! I'd been sent back to bed but now I sneaked out and peeked around the door. Mum was blocking my view, so I moved closer to see what Dad was carefully placing on the couch. It moaned … and then a voice I recognised said, 'Thanks, Mr Booth, I was afraid I'd have to spend all night in that spooky place too'.

Midnight Meeting

'Nathan!' I yelled, forgetting that I wasn't meant to be out of bed. 'What are you doing here? I looked everywhere for you guys!'

'Seeing that you are awake, Douglas, you can come in and we can all hear Nathan's story while I take a look at his injured ankle,' said Mum.

Nathan began to tell my parents all about the dare while Mum bandaged his ankle. It seems that he'd come to meet me as planned, just to let me know that Steve and Daniel had chickened out and were all for letting me go by myself—without letting me know. (Well they could hardly ring just before midnight to say 'It's been called off', could they?) I felt grateful for Nathan being good enough to want to let me know, even if he didn't manage to in the end.

'Well, how come I didn't see you, Nathan?' I asked. 'And did you see that ghost?'

Dad laughed loudly. I looked at him. 'What's the matter, Dad?' I thought to myself. He must have guessed what I was thinking because he explained the reason for his mirth.

'That wasn't a ghost, Douglas. That was Nathan, a very scared Nathan by the sounds of things. It appears that Nathan sprained his ankle. He took shelter from the oncoming storm in the church, as you did. He either fainted from the pain or he fell asleep, only to be awakened by what he thought was the ghost … which happened to be you! You both let out yells, scaring each other half to death, and then before he could tell you who it was, Douglas (once he'd realised it was you), you'd taken off like a rocket for home.'

We looked sheepishly at each other, then burst out laughing.

'Well, you did sound like a ghost,' I told him.

'So did you, you know,' he said.

We both agreed not to tell anyone else about our ghostly midnight adventure because it seemed kind of silly, scaring each other like that (although at the time it seemed more like terrifying).

Dad rang Nathan's dad up to tell him he was OK, but I guess he wasn't too OK after his dad came and picked him up—it was 2 o'clock in the morning after all! I think he probably got an earful like I did. We were grounded for a week, and I'm not allowed to even get near Dad's video camera.

I'll tell you something else—I never let myself get dragged into dares any more, even if I get called a chicken, and I'm a bit more choosy about who I call my friends now. At least I know I can trust my best friend, Nathan. After all, we did have a really scary adventure together, didn't we?

Oops, that reminds me, he's coming here soon so we can work on our homework together. We're writing a story. It's going to be called 'Midnight Meeting!'.

Midnight Meeting

A. Tick the circle that gives the best answer for each question.

1. Why did Douglas go to the graveyard?

⃝ (a) Douglas and his friends were making a scary video.

⃝ (b) Douglas wanted to see if there were any ghosts in the graveyard.

⃝ (c) Douglas and his friends had dared each other to go there.

⃝ (d) Douglas and Nathan were meeting for a midnight feast.

2. Why did Dad go back to the graveyard?

⃝ (a) To collect the video camera Douglas had dropped.

⃝ (b) To see what had really scared Douglas.

⃝ (c) To see the ghost for himself.

⃝ (d) To check Douglas hadn't broken anything.

3. How did Douglas know it was Nathan on the couch?

⃝ (a) He recognised his voice.

⃝ (b) He saw Dad carrying him in.

⃝ (c) Nathan called out to him.

⃝ (d) He guessed who it was.

4. What happened to his dad's video camera?

⃝ (a) Douglas dropped it in the graveyard.

⃝ (b) It got wet in the storm.

⃝ (c) Douglas left it in the church.

⃝ (d) Douglas returned home with it under his parka.

5. How did Douglas feel about the incident?

⃝ (a) scared

⃝ (b) ashamed

⃝ (c) embarrassed

⃝ (d) unaffected

⃝ (e) proud

Give a reason for your answer. _____

_____

_____

Midnight Meeting

B. Complete each question as required.

1. (a) What were the consequences (the results) for the boys of their midnight meeting?

_____

_____

_____

(b) Do you think these consequences were fair? Why/Why not?

_____

_____

_____

2. What did Douglas learn from this experience?

_____

_____

_____

3. Compound words are two separate words joined together to make one, e.g. flash/light. Find at least 10 in the story.

_____

_____

_____

_____

4. Find the meaning of these words.

(a) tangible – _____

(b) instinct – _____

(c) provoked – _____

(d) sheepishly – _____

(e) mirth – _____

Extra Help

Jason tried not to notice the whispering and giggling that was going on around him. He was so ashamed. Why did he have to be sent to a special teacher for extra help anyway? Sure he wasn't good with writing and reading, but so what? He still did his work. He still managed, didn't he? And now all the class thought he was a dummy. Well … that's what they were thinking. Sometimes he did, too. He'd always had to work really hard just to keep up with the rest of the class. But he never did his homework. He hated it. And now he had to go to a special class for 'special kids'.

The next morning Jason walked into a small room at the back of his classroom while all the other children were starting to write their stories. Some of them saw him leave and pointed and giggled. Jason was quite scared, but he wasn't going to show it. He didn't know the teacher sitting at the table, and he didn't know what to expect. New things were scary for him. The teacher looked up as he came in and smiled. That made him feel a bit better.

'Good morning, I'm Mrs Brown and you must be Jason. Come in.'

'It's a funny class,' he thought. 'Just the two of us.' He was sure he wouldn't get the chance to daydream here! Mrs Brown asked him what he liked about school.

'I like art. I like sports too,' he answered.

'That's great, Jason. Sports are good for you, and people are usually best at doing what they like. But reading and writing are very important as well, so I'm going to try to help you with them. But you have to help yourself too, OK? You will have to do the homework I give you every day.'

Jason groaned, 'Oh no. Not more homework to do!'.

'Don't worry, it won't be a lot and it won't be hard, but it will help you very much if you do it. You need to understand something, Jason. I can teach you things … but I can't make you learn them. That's up to you. When you do your homework, you're not doing it for me, you're doing it to help you.'

'Now then, in the lessons we will be doing different things. We'll have a bit of fun and games.' (Jason looked doubtful … games and fun in class?) 'And we'll have some spelling skills to learn,' Mrs Brown continued. 'You remember when you were learning to play rugby? You had to learn things like how to pass the ball, how to make a try, and which way to run so you wouldn't score a try for the other team.'

Jason nodded, thinking, 'What's rugby got to do with spelling?'.

'Well, those things are called skills. Rugby skills. I'll be showing you reading and writing skills.'

Jason was quiet. He just listened. He wasn't sure he could learn 'skills'. Mrs Brown was nice, though. She was friendly and she smiled a lot. She talked a lot, too!

'Did you know that the English language is really a mess? That's why it's so hard to learn.' (Jason wondered if she was supposed to say that.) 'It's a mix of many other languages. It's a wonder anyone can learn it. But there are some rules we can learn that can help us.'

Then she said, 'Kids know how to write a big "B", but they mix up a small "b" with a "d". ('I do that!' thought Jason.) 'To remember how to write a small "b", you pretend you are writing a big "B", but you leave off the top bubble.'

Extra Help

'I can remember that,' he thought. 'Maybe I can learn skills after all.'

For the first term Jason was very shy and quiet. He was scared of saying the wrong things. But Mrs Brown gave him time to think. She waited.

One day, she waited and waited for Jason to answer and then she said, 'Jason you don't have to be right all of the time. No-one is. No-one ever has all the right answers. The important thing is that you try. I'm not going to be angry if you get it wrong. We learn from our mistakes; that's how people learn best'. After that Jason started talking more to Mrs Brown. He wasn't so shy anymore.

The games they played were fun. Jason liked the word quiz best. The teacher would time him to see how fast he could read the word cards. He liked to beat his last time. Any he got wrong they looked at afterwards. He loved that quiz. He knew it was kind of a test but it was still fun. Jason was surprised to find that his homework was easy and fun. Sometimes she gave him homework sheets with puzzles and word or picture games. It was still all to do with spelling rules of course, but Jason didn't care … he loved them. He showed them to his classmates. (He even forgot to be embarrassed about his 'special' class!) The other kids thought they were great; they wanted some, too. They saw the games … and they wanted to play, too!

So in the morning before the bell went, Mrs Brown would have a whole heap of kids in her room wanting to play the word quiz or games. 'Jason knows the rules so he can teach them to you,' she'd said. Jason felt important because the others listened to him. When the bell went they had to leave and he stayed. 'Good,' he thought. 'I like my special class where I'm the only kid and the teacher takes a lot of notice of me.'

'Mrs Brown, Mrs Brown, can I come to your class?'

'Me too, can I come too?' The children were crowding around her. She looked down and smiled at them. 'I'm sorry, but I can only manage to teach a few lucky children, so I have to have the ones who need my help the most.'

They walked away sadly, muttering, 'Lucky Jason he gets all the fun!'.

It was now the last week of the second term and Mrs Brown was talking to Jason.

Mrs Brown was saying, 'It seems you are just too good for me now, Jason, they want me to help another boy. You've done all the homework, and it's really helped you. You've learnt all the skills you need to keep up with your class. Now, you must remember to use those skills'.

'No …,' he thought. 'That's not fair!'

'Your teacher tells me you have more confidence in yourself and he has noticed you are trying now to answer maths questions that you wouldn't try before. And … he said that you're getting a lot of them right! That's terrific, Jason, I'm so proud of you,' Mrs Brown continued.

Jason grinned. 'Not half as proud as I am of myself,' he thought, pleased with the praise.

'Do you remember what I said when we first started?' She waited for his answer.

Jason thought back to his first day. He remembered the giggles and stares. And he remembered what she'd said.

'You mean when you said you could teach me skills but I had to learn them?' He grinned. 'I guess I did learn them, right?'

'You sure did, Jason, you sure did!'

Extra Help

A. Tick the circle that gives the best answer for each question.

1. When Mrs Brown asked Jason what he liked about school, what did he reply?

- ○ (a) maths and sports
- ○ (b) art and sports
- ○ (c) reading and science
- ○ (d) sports and music
- ○ (e) reading and writing

2. What was it that made Jason feel a bit better about the teacher when he first saw her?

- ○ (a) She had a kind face.
- ○ (b) She wasn't old.
- ○ (c) She smiled at him.
- ○ (d) She had a nice blouse on.
- ○ (e) She had curly hair.

3. Which words best describe how Jason was feeling during his first lesson?

- ○ (a) confused, doubtful, quiet, nervous
- ○ (b) confused, angry, talkative, anxious
- ○ (c) clear, doubtful, talkative, calm
- ○ (d) confused, doubtful, talkative, calm

4. Which activity did Jason like best?

- ○ (a) homework
- ○ (b) picture games
- ○ (c) word quiz
- ○ (d) puzzles
- ○ (e) writing

5. Why do you think Mrs Brown let the other children play with the games before school?

- ○ (a) Because they needed help with their reading and writing, too.
- ○ (b) To give Jason more practice.
- ○ (c) To help the other children understand what she did.
- ○ (d) So they could try the games out to see if they worked.
- ○ (e) Because they were at school early.

Extra Help

B. Complete each question as required.

1. Number the events as they occurred in the story.

- ☐ (a) He taught his classmates the word quiz.
- ☐ (b) Jason found out he was attending a special class.
- ☐ (c) Mrs Brown told him he didn't have to be right all the time.
- ☐ (d) Jason met Mrs Brown.
- ☐ (e) Jason's maths also improved.

2. Explain how Jason's feelings about his extra help changed over time.

_____

_____

_____

3. 'We learn from our mistakes, that's how people learn best.'
Do you agree or disagree with this statement? Say why.

_____

_____

_____

_____

4. Think of four words which describe Mrs Brown.

(a) _____   (b) _____

(c) _____   (d) _____

5. Find a synonym in the story for these words.

(a) grinned – _____

(b) moaned – _____

(c) laughed – _____

(d) incorrect – _____

(e) afraid – _____

6. Find an antonym in the story for these words.

(a) easy – _____

(b) same – _____

(c) noisy – _____

(d) forget – _____

(e) afternoon – _____

Answers

Pages 1–3 A Lesson in History

A. 1. (b)   2. (b)   3. (b)   4. (e)   5. (b)
B. 1. She stood in the water trembling, despite the hot sun.
   2. Teacher check
   3. Teacher check
   4. (a) the incident at the beach
      (b) the incident at the pool
      (c) learning to swim at swimming classes
   5. Teacher check

Pages 4–6 Jokeman

A. 1. (c)   2. (b)   3. (a)   4. (b)   5. (c)
B. 1. (a) false (b) true (c) false (d) false (e) true
     (f) false
   2.

new	old
smiling	frowning
happy	sad
last	first
answered	questioned
finished	begun/started

   3. (a) serious (b) humour (c) giggled (d) brother
   4. Teacher check

Pages 7–9 Skateboard Star

A. 1. (a)   2. (d)   3. (b)   4. (d)
B. 1. (b) (d) (e) (c) (a)
   2. Teacher check
   3. Teacher check
   4. Teacher check
   5. Teacher check

Pages 10–12 Melissa's Story

A. 1. (d)   2. (b)   3. (a)   4. (b)   5. (c)
B. 1. (a) Matthew (b) Melissa's brother.
   2. (a) true (b) false (c) false (d) true (e) false
   3. Teacher check
   4.

adjectives	nouns
rare bird's	eggs
living	creatures
china	cabinets
oldest	child/kid
Chinese	medicines

   5. Teacher check

Pages 13–15 Best Friends

A. 1. (b)   2. (b)   3. (c)   4. (d)   5. (e)
B. 1. (c) (b) (d) (e) (a)
   2. Teacher check
   3. Teacher check
   4. (a) dirty – filthy/unclean
      (b) big – large/huge
      (c) worried – stressed/anxious
      (d) right – correct
   5. (a) panic – a sudden terror
      (b) missile – an object or weapon that can be
         thrown or shot
      (c) loan – money given for a short time, to be
         repaid with interest
      (d) imagine – to form a picture in the mind
   6.

pays money to ...	pays money for ...
owner of the shop	rent
newspaper, signwriter	advertising
electricity company	electricity
manufacturer	bicycles
the bank	loan

Pages 16–18 The Secret Wish

A. 1. (c)   2. (c)   3. (a)   4. (b)   5. (b)
B. 1. (a) she wore outrageous clothes
      (b) she rode a 10-speed bike
      (c) she enjoyed playing spacies with Corey
   2. (a) false (b) false (c) false (d) true (e) true
   3. (a) Dane decided to teach his mum how to use a
         computer
      (b) his mum became engrossed in playing
         computer games
      (c) his mum began to use the computer to write
         stories
   4. (a) outrageous – something that shocks or may
         offend some people
      (b) anxiously – full of worry
      (c) arcade – a covered passage with shops on
         either side
      (d) total – complete or absolute
   5. Teacher check

Pages 19–21 Kid Sister

A. 1. (e)   2. (e)   3. (b)   4. (b)   5. (e)
B. 1. Teacher check
   2. (a) perhaps (b) yes (c) yes (d) no
   3. Teacher check
   4. Teacher check

Pages 22–24 No Party for Blake

A. 1. (d)   2. (d)   3. (c)   4. (c)
B. 1. (a) (b) (e) (c) (d)
   2. (a) ... no-one seemed to want him to join in
      (b) ... she was worried about him being so quiet
      (c) ... you got to eat the jellybeans at the end
   3. Teacher check
   4. (a) The kids all lined up quietly when the Cub
        leader shouted 'pack, pack, pack!'.
      (b) There were girls at Cubs.
      (c) He enjoyed himself.
   5. (a) perfect (b) bunch (c) normal (d) proud
   6. Teacher check

Pages 25–28 Midnight Meeting

A. 1. (c)   2. (b)   3. (a)   4. (d)   5. (c)
B. 1. (a) They were grounded for a week and Douglas
        wasn't allowed to use Dad's video camera.
      (b) Teacher check
   2. Teacher check
   3. midnight, graveyard, headstones, everywhere,
      inside, anything, something, nightmare, hallway,
      raincoat, himself, awake, oncoming, homework,
      nothing, whatever, carefully, without
   4. (a) tangible – real, able to be touched or felt
      (b) instinct – a natural urge or tendency
      (c) provoked – to urge or incite to action
      (d) sheepishly – awkwardly shy, embarrassingly
      (e) mirth – amusement and laughter

Pages 29–32 Extra Help

A. 1. (b)   2. (c)   3. (a)   4. (c)   5. (c)
B. 1. (b) (d) (c) (a) (e)
   2. Teacher check
   3. Teacher check
   4. Teacher check
   5. (a) smiled (b) groaned (c) giggled
      (d) wrong (e) scared
   6. (a) hard (b) different (c) quiet
      (d) remember (e) morning